Counting

Words by Sue Graves

Illustrations by Jan Smith

book-studio

Jim the spaceman is going into space in a rocket.

His friends wave goodbye.

Count the rockets.

How many of Jim's friends can you see?

Jim's rocket zooms past some big, yellow moons and some beautiful shooting stars.

Count the moons.

How many shooting stars can you see?

Jim lands his rocket
on Planet Rock.

Some little green men
come to meet him.

Count the little green men.

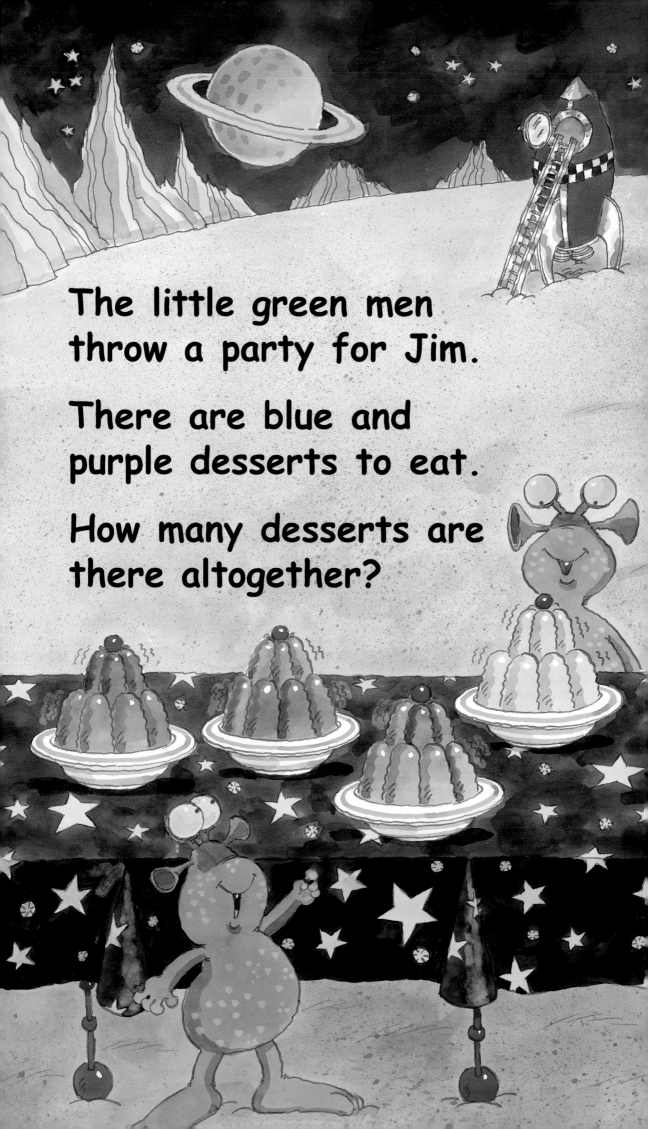

The little green men throw a party for Jim.

There are blue and purple desserts to eat.

How many desserts are there altogether?

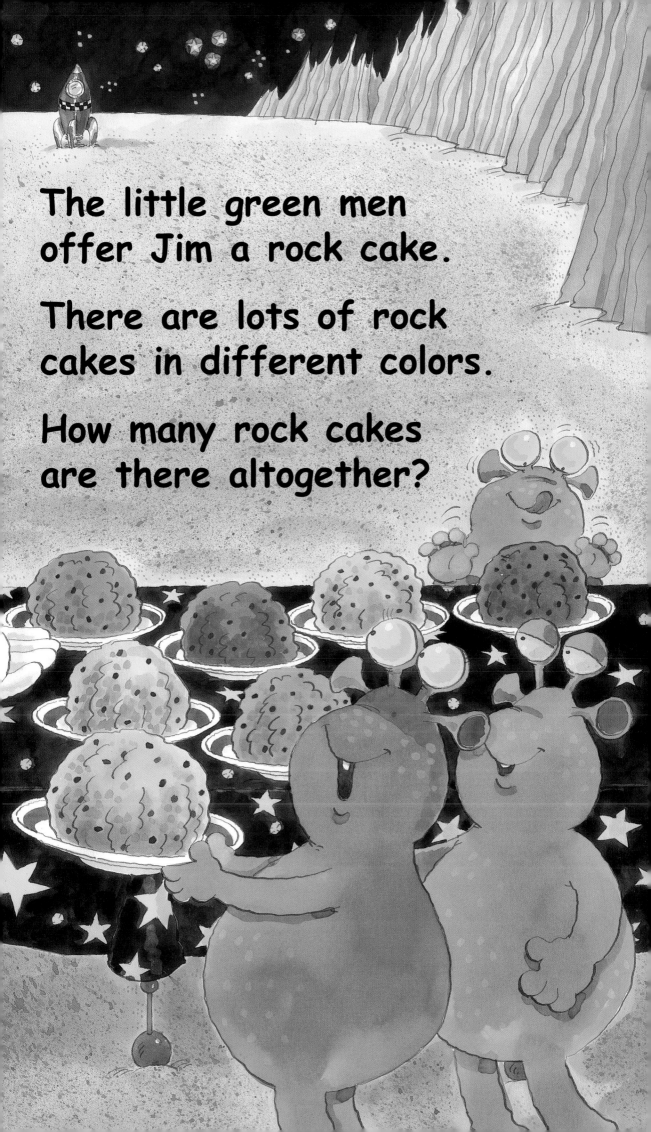

The little green men offer Jim a rock cake.

There are lots of rock cakes in different colors.

How many rock cakes are there altogether?

Jim has some toys for the little green men.

He gives them silver spaceships.

Count the silver spaceships.

The little green men take
Jim on a tour of Planet Rock.

They show Jim their little
planet pets.

How many planet pets
can you see?

"I have to go now," says Jim.

He fills the rocket with cans of gas.

Count the cans of gas.

"Count down to blast off!" says Jim.

The little green men count down to blast off.

Help the little green men count down.

10-9-8-7-6
5-4-3-2-1
BLAST OFF!

The end